Exploring Personality Type

Discovering My Best and Your Best

BY ELIZABETH MURPHY

C A P T

CENTER FOR APPLICATIONS OF PSYCHOLOGICAL TYPE, Inc.
2815 NW 13th St., Suite 401 · Gainesville, FL 32609 · 1.800.777.2278 · www.capt.org

Published by
Center for Applications of Psychological Type, Inc.
2815 NW 13th Street, Suite 401
Gainesville, FL 32609
352.375.0160
www.capt.org

Center for Applications of Psychological Type, Inc. and CAPT are trademarks or registered trademarks of the Center for Applications of Psychological Type in the United States and other countries.

Murphy-Meisgeier Type Indicator for Children and MMTIC are trademarks or registered trademarks of Elizabeth Murphy and Charles Meisgeier in the United States and other countries.

Library of Congress Cataloging-in-Publication Data

Murphy, Elizabeth, 1949-

  Exploring personality type : discovering my best and your best / by

Elizabeth Murphy.

      p. cm.

  ISBN-13: 978-0-935652-83-3 (pbk.)

  ISBN-10: 0-935652-83-3 (pbk.)

  1. Personality. 2. Typology (Psychology) 3. Myers-Briggs Type

Indicator. I. Title.

  BF698.3.M875 2008

  158.1--dc22

2008026814

TABLE OF CONTENTS

1

2

3

1

INTRODUCTION TO DISCOVERING YOUR PERSONALITY DIFFERENCES

This booklet offers an opportunity to learn about your best ways and the best ways of others. Normal personality patterns are associated with identified strategies and tasks. Those that match our natural preferences are easier and those that do not match our natural preferences are more difficult to master. The ones that are more difficult take more energy or more work to be successful, but success is possible for all. **Knowing your best path for success and knowing when you have to work harder to achieve success gives you a better handle on the best strategy to use for the situation or task.**

Just as you have two hands but prefer one, you have opposite personality preferences but favor one over the other. By learning about these differences you can learn to know yourself better and to manage yourself to do whatever is expected. Success and competence belong to all types.

This booklet is intended to help you identify your strengths and stretches. Through using this information you will discover your preferences and learn to value others who are different from you. As you learn about type, you will have a chance to develop personal goals to help you improve your study skills, your relationship skills, and your interaction with parents and teachers. You will have a chance to explore new ideas and new strategies for personal success.

Please note that this booklet is meant to be used with a teacher or parent or in group settings with a facilitator, who will have the guidelines and instructions for understanding the information and who will lead the exercises to help you learn more about personality type.

Enjoy the experience!

Goals for Understanding Type Differences

The more we understand ourselves, the better we can handle our

learning and living challenges and the more we can respect that everyone

can be different but still be good learners and good friends.

Learning about type you will develop . . .

◄● Self-awareness

Self-management ↑

Respect for differences ●►

2

STEPS FOR LEARNING ABOUT AND UNDERSTANDING TYPE

People climb **_up_** steps.
Start at the **_bottom_** and work your way to the top!

8 Use this information to help with working with teachers, parents, and others who are important to you.

7 Use this information to help with friendships with people your age and with adults.

6 Use this information to be a better team member.

5 Use this information to plan study habits.

4 Explore some next steps for using type information.

3 Verify which type is most like you.

2 Learn about type differences.

start here ◆→ **1** Take the Murphy-Meisgeier Type Indicator for Children® (MMTIC™) assessment. You completed **Step 1** when you answered the MMTIC questions. Now on to **Step 2 . . .**

STEP 2
Learn about Type Differences

Each person has a best way . . .

➨ To learn.

➨ To form friendships.

➨ To organize their work and play.

A person's personality type **describes . . .**

➨ The normal and good differences that exist among people.

➨ Your best way of working and living with others.

your Strengths { Sometimes you do what you think is best and it also happens to be **easy for you.** It is easy because you used your personality strengths.

Sometimes you do what you think is best, even if it takes **more work.** It is more work because you used your personality stretches. } **your stretches**

Your *Strengths* and *Stretches* can help you ▪ ▪ ▪ ▪ ▪

1) Understand and get along better with people.

2) Know yourself so you can use your strengths when possible and get help with your stretches when necessary.

3) Study and learn better on your own.

4) Work with friends better.

5) Learn how to ask for help when you need it.

6) Understand when you will need to stretch to do your best.

Always understand that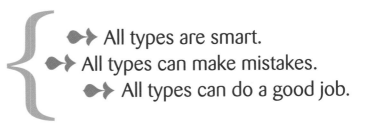

- ➜ All types are smart.
- ➜ All types can make mistakes.
- ➜ All types can do a good job.

All types are good. Your type preferences might be different than your friends' or families' preferences. This is normal. Your type gives you a special energy to do things the best way for you, even if that is different than how others would choose to act. Knowing your personality helps you find the way that works best for you.

IMPORTANT

1) A personality type does not tell what you will think, do, or say. You choose your behavior.

2) You do not choose what your strengths or stretches will be. You are born with those preferences. Your strengths are things that come easily and your stretches are things that may be a challenge.

TYPE VERIFICATION ACTIVITY

"I Am a Good Student"

Select the description of the student that BEST describes you. Both are effective learners.

[CIRCLE ONE]

- I raise my hand a lot to talk. I like hearing what I say.

- I like to study with friends so we can tell each other what we know.

- I like some noise while I am working. Too quiet is boring.

- I like it when people let me keep talking until my idea makes sense.

- - - *O R* - - -

- I raise my hand when I have a good idea or when I know the answer. I don't like it when two people talk at the same time.

- I like to study on my own because too much noise distracts me.

- I like to know what I want to say before I raise my hand.

- In a new class, I am usually quiet until I get to know the teacher and the other students.

NOTE: *This type verification activity is to be used as a method for verifying type only after the MMTIC assessment has been administered. Preference descriptions are not a reliable and valid method for measuring psychological type and should not be used in this manner.*

TYPE VERIFICATION ACTIVITY

"I Am a Good Student"

2

Select the description of the student that BEST describes you. Both are effective learners.

[C I R C L E   O N E]

- I like information. Lots of information makes an idea become clearer.
- I like clear directions. I want the teacher to tell me what to do and how to do it.
- I like it best when we study a little bit and then try to use what we learned.
- I like going over things we already know to prove we still know it well.
- I like making the project more than coming up with the idea for the project.

- - - **O R** - - -

- I have to work hard to remember facts. I know what I mean but sometimes forget the details.
- I like coming up with ideas. That part is fun. Making the project is more work for me.
- I like thinking up ideas that make my project special and different.
- I like doing things in a different way than others in the class.

NOTE: This type verification activity is to be used as a method for verifying type only after the MMTIC assessment has been administered. Preference descriptions are not a reliable and valid method for measuring psychological type and should not be used in this manner.

MMTIC Preference Icons © 2008 Center for Applications of Psychological Type

"I Am a Good Student"

Select the description of the student that
BEST describes you. Both are effective learners.

[C I R C L E   O N E]

- I like to figure things out.
- It is easy for me if I put information into groups.
- I know what I do well and don't want to have to worry about a teammate who can't do the work as well.
- I like to ask why and I tend to tell people just what I am thinking. Sometimes people get upset with me for what I say when it was just the truth.
- I make choices based on what seems logical and makes the most sense.

- - - O R - - -

- I like working with my friends on teams. Cooperating with others is easy for me.
- I like helping everyone on the team do their parts.
- I like when people are warm and friendly and give lots of compliments. I think it is important to tell people how well they are doing.
- I make choices based on what I think is important. I don't care if that means it is logical or not.
- I help people because I care.

NOTE: *This type verification activity is to be used as a method for verifying type only after the MMTIC assessment has been administered. Preference descriptions are not a reliable and valid method for measuring psychological type and should not be used in this manner.*

TYPE VERIFICATION ACTIVITY

"I Am a Good Student"

Select the description of the student that BEST describes you. Both are effective learners.

[CIRCLE ONE]

- I like to plan. I make a plan for how to study and I like to follow that plan.
- I like to know what is going to happen.
- When a teacher gives an assignment I like to get started right away.
- I do not like working when the due date is near. I am always afraid I won't be done on time. Getting my work done first is important. Then I can relax and have free time for fun.

- - - OR - - -

- I might make a plan but I want to be able to change it if I need or want to.
- I like to be ready but not too early. If I do the work too soon I might not do my best.
- I like working at the last minute. My best ideas seem to come when the due date is near. When it is time to be done I will be.
- I know I have to do work but work can be fun too. The work may take a little longer but adding the fun is worth it.

NOTE: This type verification activity is to be used as a method for verifying type only after the MMTIC assessment has been administered. Preference descriptions are not a reliable and valid method for measuring psychological type and should not be used in this manner.

What do we know about all types?

You have a style that works for you. Others have a style that works for them. No matter what your style there are things we know to be true. Some are listed here.

- ●➤ There are many ways to do a job well.

- ●➤ There are many ways to contribute to a team.

- ●➤ There are many ways to talk with others to make our ideas heard clearly.

- ●➤ There are many ways to design new ideas.

- ●➤ There are many ways to make our ideas work.

- ●➤ We can all be good at our job. We just might have to work harder than others at different times.

Knowing about ourselves and others allows us to . . .

◄● Work well with others.

Use our energy best. ●➤

◄● Value others.

Next, your teacher, parent, or other adult will introduce you to personality type differences. After you finish learning about differences, you can continue with the other steps.

Learning about personality differences

On the following pages, you will read descriptions of eight different choices people make about how they do things. The choices are grouped in pairs, and people prefer one in the pair better than the other.

People who prefer Extraversion (E) . . .

- Like working with many friends
- Like talking out loud while they think
- Get tired when listening
- Must talk about it when upset, angry, or embarrassed
- Get energy by doing, being active
- Act . . . then think
- Are ready to try new ideas

People who prefer Introversion (I) . . .

- Like working on their own or with a few others
- Like thinking inside and then telling
- Get tired doing things with others for a long time
- Have a hard time when upset, angry, or embarrassed
- Get energy by taking time alone
- Think . . . and then act
- Hesitate in new situations and with new thoughts

MMTIC Preference Icons © 2008 Center for Applications of Psychological Type

People who prefer Sensing (S) . . .

- Like information presented in order
- Like complete directions
- Like to know all the facts to understand the whole idea
- Like producing more than designing
- Like many examples to prove a point
- Think sequentially (in order)
- Focus on and remember details
- Value experience to understand learning

People who prefer Intuition (N) . . .

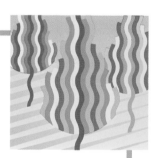

- Like to learn lots of different things different ways
- Like few directions so they can do it their way
- Like to know the main idea but may miss details
- Like making up the idea more than producing it
- Like only a few examples to prove a point
- Look for patterns, connections, themes
- Read for the main idea; skim naturally
- May have trouble producing or building what they design

People who prefer Thinking (T) . . .

- Enjoy personal challenges
- Ask "why" and need to understand "why"
- Tell the truth as they see it and sometimes hurt the feelings of others with their truth
- Like to solve problems
- Work hard to be the best
- Are independent decision makers
- Use logic and analysis to understand
- Demand competence in self and others
- Notice what is wrong first and then what is right

People who prefer Feeling (F) . . .

- Enjoy cooperating with others
- Trust others to help in good ways
- Are sensitive to the feelings of others and careful not to say things they think might hurt others
- Like to help people
- Work hard to do their best
- Make decisions based on their values
- Are concerned with harmony
- Need feedback and find acceptance important
- Notice what is right first, then what is wrong

People who prefer Judging (J) . . .

- Like to plan and like to use their plan
- Like to get things done
- Like to know what will happen next
- Cannot focus if a due date is near and the work is not done
- Want to complete one project before beginning another
- Control their world by planning ahead
- Work first, then relax and have fun
- Like to reach decisions quickly

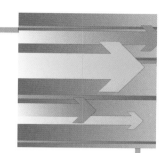

People who prefer Perceiving (P) . . .

- Like to be flexible and change if needed
- Like to play around while getting work done
- Like to be surprised; to explore
- Focus better when the due date is closer
- May start too many projects but complete them when they are due
- Play around while working and get more done that way
- Like to keep choices open until the last moment
- Control their world by being adaptable and flexible

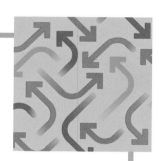

STEP 3
Which Type is Most Like You

Your teacher, parent, or other adult will give you your MMTIC results. Mark your activity choice and your MMTIC choice. Then mark which type you believe describes you best.

On the I Am a Good Student activity you chose:

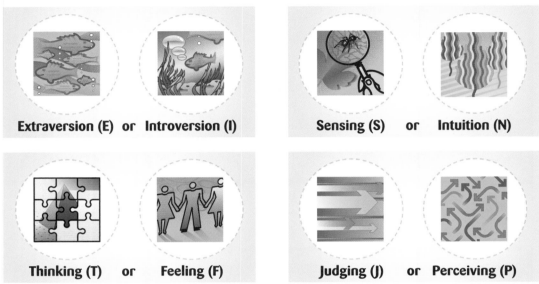

Now that you have learned about type, your teacher, parent, or other adult will give you your MMTIC results. On the MMTIC you scored:

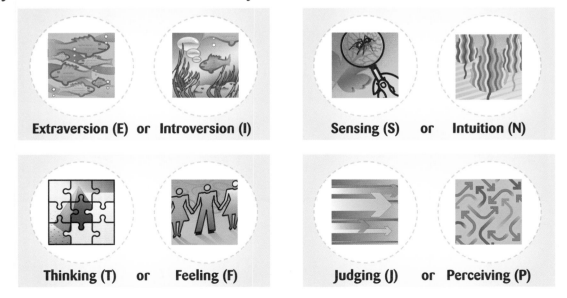

MMTIC Preference Icons © 2008 Center for Applications of Psychological Type

Think of your answers on the *I Am a Good Student* activity, your answers on the MMTIC, and the lessons describing type differences. Now choose which descriptions match you best.

These describe me best:

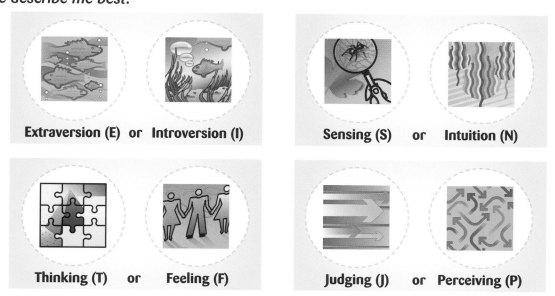

My four-letter type preferences are:

(If you have not yet decided on a preference, leave that space blank. You can take as long as you wish to decide.)

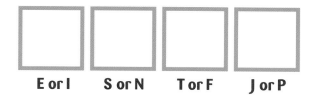

Once you know your preferences, you can use this information in lots of different ways:

➻ *To help you know how to study best for you.*

➻ *To help you work better with people of all types.*

➻ *To help you make good choices and decisions.*

STEP 4
The Next Steps

Now that you understand about differences, you will be able to use this information in many ways. For instance, you can:

1) Develop smarter study habits.

2) Develop kinder and more effective team skills.

3) Demonstrate an appreciation and respect for the adults in your life who are ready to help you.

4) Help your teacher, parents, and other family members understand you better.

On the next few pages, you will be asked to share how the information about your personality helps you perform.

You will learn how to use this information during the school year to help you consider the four primary sides of learning:

1) What are the critical and valuable **facts** to know?

2) What ideas and **themes** do these facts support?

3) **Why** did something happen and what are the **cause and effects?**

4) Why is what I am learning **important to people** and to the world?

Every time you study you will want to ask yourself to identify the facts, name the themes, explain how and why, and name why this information is important. If you can answer these four questions about each thing you learn this year, you will do better . . . and that's a reason to celebrate differences!

Making good decisions

To make your best decision, ask yourself the questions from each of the four main ways of looking at choices. Use these questions to organize your learning or to help you solve problems.

SENSING

- What do I know? What are the facts?
- What does common sense suggest?
- What are the benefits?
- What will this cost?
- What are we doing now that is working?
- What has already been tried? Can we modify that?
- What have others done in similar circumstances?

INTUITION

- What else is possible?
- What are other ways to evaluate this?
- What are some new ideas yet to be tried?
- Are there patterns in the facts?
- Are there connections between certain facts?
- Are there sets of rules to follow that will let this make sense?
- Is there a new and innovative way to solve this or answer this question?

THINKING

- What would be a right way or a better way to do this?
- What is wrong with each idea?
- Why should this be done?
- What are the consequences with each alternative?
- What is the logical way to present the problem?
- What is the logical way to present possible solutions?
- Can this be done in a reasonable amount of time?
- What are the consequences of not doing anything?

FEELING

- Did we get ideas from everyone involved?
- What is good about each idea?
- What hunches do you have about how others will react?
- How will this answer impact others?
- Does the choice match what you think is important?
- How much do I care about what might happen?
- Will my decision make others feel better or worse?
- Who will help me if I need help with my choice?

STEP 5
My Study Strengths and Goals

Now I know that my study strengths are

1) _____

2) _____

3) _____

goal | **Each week I will learn one new skill to help me study smarter.**

Write in each week what you will try for the next seven days. Only make your goals for one week at a time.

(Week 1) I will _____

(Week 2) I will _____

(Week 3) I will _____

(Week 4) I will _____

(Week 5) I will _____

(Week 6) I will _____

(Week 7) I will _____

(Week 8) I will _____

(Week 9) I will _____

(Week 10) I will _____

Since you now know your four-letter type preferences, you can get some hints about learning skills by reading suggestions for your type *(see pages 26–41).*

STEP 6
My Teamwork Strengths and Goals

Now I know that my teamwork strengths are

1) _____

2) _____

3) _____

goal | Each week I will learn one new skill to help me be a better team member.

Write in each week what you will try for the next seven days. Only make your goals for one week at a time.

(Week 1)   I will _____

(Week 2)   I will _____

(Week 3)   I will _____

(Week 4)   I will _____

(Week 5)   I will _____

(Week 6)   I will _____

(Week 7)   I will _____

(Week 8)   I will _____

(Week 9)   I will _____

(Week 10) I will _____

Since you now know your four-letter type preferences, you can get some hints about working with others by reading suggestions for your type *(see pages 26–41)*.

STEP 7
My Relationship Strengths and Goals

Now I know that my relationship strengths with people my age and with adults, are

1) _____

2) _____

3) _____

goal **Each week I will learn one new skill to help me enjoy relationships with people my age and with adults.**

Write in each week what you will try for the next seven days. Only make your goals for one week at a time.

(Week 1) I will _____

(Week 2) I will _____

(Week 3) I will _____

(Week 4) I will _____

(Week 5) I will _____

(Week 6) I will _____

(Week 7) I will _____

(Week 8) I will _____

(Week 9) I will _____

(Week 10) I will _____

Since you now know your four-letter type preferences, you can get some hints about skills you can try for being with others by reading suggestions for your type *(see pages 26–41).*

STEP 8
A Guide for My Teachers, My Parents, and Me

There are times in every classroom or when I'm doing my homework when I might get confused about the material we are studying. There may be times when my behavior gets off task. If either of these happens, the following ideas are the best ways to help me get refocused on my work.

When I am confused about homework or the material we are studying it will help me to learn if you . . .

1) _____

2) _____

3) _____

4) _____

5) _____

If I happen to get off task or disruptive with my behavior the best way to get me back on task is to . . . *(start your idea with an action word—a verb)*

1) _____

2) _____

3) _____

Parent/Teacher Team Support: It helps when teachers, parents, and students agree on a plan. Show this page to your parent and teacher and ask them to sign if they agree.

As this child's parent or teacher I agree with the above choices and will support this child by implementing similar strategies at home and at school.

_____   _____   _____
PARENT   TEACHER   DATE

Congratulations! You reached the top of the stairs

You now have more tools to help you study smarter, work with others more effectively, and relate to your parents and teachers in ways that show your love or respect.

Here are a few key points to remember about personality type:

- Personality preferences are about energy not behavior. People can behave any way they need to but some will use more energy than others to do similar things.

- Personality is no excuse for failing to do a job.

- Personality develops over a lifetime. Natural preferences develop as a person learns how to control choices and to recognize what is needed.

- Personality preferences each have natural strengths and stretches that make some tasks easy and some more difficult.

- No one personality preference is better than another.

- Your personality never limits your choices. A person cannot be denied an opportunity because of his or her chosen personality preferences.

- Your environment influences the development of your preferences but the preferences are in you when you are born.

- Understanding your preferences gives individuals opportunities to know and understand their learning and living style preferences.

3

SUGGESTIONS FOR THE SIXTEEN TYPES
JOURNAL LOGS

On the following pages, you will find suggestions for the sixteen types and how they best approach studying, friendships, working with others, and getting along with parents and teachers. Read your own suggestions, and then read the suggestions

Suggestions for the Sixteen Personality Types

for other types so you can get an idea of how you may be different from your friends, teachers, and parents in how you best like to work, play, and study.

ENFP

Suggestions to help you with your strengths and work with your stretches

Suggestions for *Studying*

- Study with a friend.
- Box off or list the main topics. Then put three to four facts under each topic.
- Skim the chapter before the teacher introduces it. After you talk about it in class, read the chapter more carefully. This way you will remember more.
- When you are watching TV, ask a parent or friend to quiz you during commercials. You can have fun remembering a little bit of information at a time.

Suggestions for *Working with Others*

- Give lots of compliments to your friends when they are working hard.
- Get excited about the idea. Then pick a partner to help you complete the project.
- Check with classmates to be sure you remember exactly what you have to do. Sometimes you get excited and think you remember everything but you forget some details.

Suggestions for *Friendships*

- Make sure you have time for your friends and time for your family. Sometimes you say yes to all your friends and then are too tired for your family.
- When a friend lets you down or hurts your feelings, let them know. They may not realize they have hurt you.
- Laugh and play and enjoy each other. Help friends who are not as outgoing as you by including them in your activities.

Suggestions for *Working with Parents and Teachers*

- Know that you may get into trouble sometimes because your curiosity takes you places that are off limits. Accept the consequence.
- Ask for feedback when you begin to doubt if someone still cares about you or your work.
- Ask the teacher for choices if the task seems boring to you. Sometimes other choices are possible if you ask.

ENTP
Suggestions to help you with your strengths and work with your stretches

Suggestions for *Studying*

- Challenge yourself to get your work done in record time.
- Use a visual organizer to help you know the most important details to remember.
- Take frequent breaks when studying material you think is boring or when you have too many things to memorize.
- Make connections between pieces of information to make them easier to remember.

Suggestions for *Working with Others*

- Enjoy what you do well. Volunteer to do these jobs.
- Ask others for their ideas even when you are confident that your ideas are good.
- Compliment your team members for their work.
- Check if your team members like to have contests as much as you. Some may not.

Suggestions for *Friendships*

- Make many friends in many places. You are interested in lots of things so find different people for each of your interests.
- Join groups that allow you to compete individually while still being part of the team.
- Let your friends see you laugh and enjoy their company. Sometimes they may not know how much you like them.

Suggestions for *Working with Parents and Teachers*

- First, tell parents that you will do what they say. Then, tell them your opinion. Sometimes when you start with your opinion they think you won't do as you are asked.
- Negotiate. Reach a compromise when you want to try something a different way.
- Resist arguing to prove your point. Sometimes you wear people out by making your point over and over again.

ESFP
Suggestions to help you with your strengths and work with your stretches

Suggestions for *Studying*

- Study with friends. They will help you to understand the concepts by offering examples.
- Study a little each day so it doesn't feel overwhelming.
- Review old learning to remind yourself how much you have mastered.
- Ask someone to help you sort the important facts from the enrichment facts. You tend to want to learn them all and can get overwhelmed.

Suggestions for *Working with Others*

- Tell others when they begin to annoy you. You usually work well with people but may not let them know when they bother you.
- Ask for help when you do not understand the ideas. Sometimes you just need a little more information.
- Keep your work in one place and get the work done on time.
- Help others to avoid arguing by setting rules for solving problems.

Suggestions for *Friendships*

- Enjoy the company of many friends. Go many places. Have fun. Have lots of experiences. Sharing activities with friends is fun for you and for them.
- Offer to help with a community service project where you can get praise for service as well as a chance to be with friends.
- Be careful to avoid getting into trouble by doing something just because your friends suggest it. Make sure their ideas are good ones before you agree to go along.

Suggestions for *Working with Parents and Teachers*

- Be truthful. Don't sneak to do something in the moment that might get you into trouble later.
- Ask for help with scheduling your work so it can be done a little at a time.
- Finish what you start or let the adult know it is not your intention to finish (when you have that choice).

ESTP
Suggestions to help you with your strengths and work with your stretches

Suggestions for *Studying*

- Study with friends. Let them help you with all the reading and you help them with ways to remember all the details.
- Plan from the due date backward to find when you need to start your work.
- Ask for examples to explain the idea.
- Study…take a break…study…take a break. Frequent breaks will help.

Suggestions for *Working with Others*

- Be prepared for the fact that others may not be as spontaneous as you and may resist some of your suggestions because they appear to be risky.
- Create contests where the other partner has an equal chance of winning.
- Recognize that sometimes when you tell the truth to others they may get their feelings hurt. Think of how the other person will feel.

Suggestions for *Friendships*

- Get to know many people. You love to have people connections everywhere you go.
- Take the lead. Your eagerness to try things may mean you jump ahead of your friends to be first. Be sure your friends are OK with that.
- Be sensitive to the feelings of others who may not have as much confidence as you. They may take longer to make decisions. Give them the time they need.

Suggestions for *Working with Parents and Teachers*

- Know that even if you think you are right the adult often has the final choice. Stay calm. Listen to them. Ask them to listen to you too.
- Ask the teacher to assign you a mentor who can challenge you to think.
- Write a contract with your parents or teachers to get the work done. Keep your word.
- Let adults introduce you to their world so you can learn about careers and adult activities.

ESFJ
Suggestions to help you with your strengths and work with your stretches

Suggestions for *Studying*

- Study with some friends to highlight the most important points that need to be learned.
- Begin studying early so you can study a little each day. Cramming does not work for you.
- Repeat your study concepts out loud. Hearing it will help you remember it.
- Use an outline or plan to get your work done.
- Finish one subject before beginning to study another.

Suggestions for *Working with Others*

- Use your natural warm and outgoing nature to help others feel comfortable working on the team.
- Use the support of the team to help you select the best ideas to try. Your strength is helping the team use the idea the group selects.
- Help the team develop a plan of action for getting everything done on time. You have a good sense of timing and can set reasonable due dates for others.

Suggestions for *Friendships*

- Save some of your energy. Your outgoing and friendly nature makes you popular with others. You may find you enroll in so many activities that you exhaust yourself physically.
- Decide first if you think you did a good job. Then ask for the opinion of others. Sometimes you can get your feelings hurt when people don't like your work.
- Try to understand competition and see how it is different from conflict. Sometimes you see it as conflict when it is just competition.

Suggestions for *Working with Parents and Teachers*

- Ask for specific directions. When a teacher's directions are vague you can get confused. You also do not like teachers to ask you to discover information on your own. If that happens ask for specific directions or ask to work with a partner.
- Plan your way and check with your parents about their plans. Your plan for getting something done can be wonderful unless your parents have a different plan. If that happens, talk to them. Decide together which plan is best or if the plans can be combined.

ESTJ
Suggestions to help you with your strengths and work with your stretches

Suggestions for *Studying*

- Talk out your ideas even if there is no one to listen. Hearing ideas out loud makes them easier to remember.
- Set personal challenges and try to meet them. You love a good contest.
- Finish one subject before starting another. You like to be done and not have more than one thing to do at a time.

Suggestions for *Working with Others*

- Wait a little while to make a choice. You like to decide quickly. Listen to ideas from friends who take longer to decide. They might have some good thoughts too.
- Tell your teammates when they are doing a good job. You know they are but you need to tell them.
- Tell others when you are thinking out loud. Tell them when your idea is your final choice.
- Volunteer to organize the information and set a schedule for getting things done. This is something you could do easily and well.

Suggestions for *Friendships*

- Play some games with friends where each of you has a fair chance to win. Even if it is not the game that you will be the best at, your friends will appreciate that you played.
- Accept that some friends may work at a different speed than you. You work first and fast and may expect your friends to work like you. Some may do a better job when they work slowly.
- Give more compliments to your friends. That is a good way of letting them know you like them.

Suggestions for *Working with Parents and Teachers*

- Tell your ideas when you disagree with what the adult says. First, tell them you agree to follow their rules, and then let them know that you just want them to also hear your ideas.
- Use your good sense of humor to help people listen to your ideas.
- Tell parents your plan for the day. Ask if the plan seems like a good idea to them. Let them know you would like to keep your plan and don't want changes, if possible.

ENFJ
Suggestions to help you with your strengths and work with your stretches

Suggestions for *Studying*

- Study with a group of friends. You will enjoy the energy of being around others and they can help you focus on the lesson to be learned.
- List the general topics to be learned and challenge yourself to name four to five facts under each topic.
- Stay on the selected topic when writing. You can get so excited about researching many ideas that your topic does not have enough details.

Suggestions for *Working with Others*

- Use your warmth and charm to make working with others an enjoyable activity.
- Help team members who argue by using your humor and gentle ways to get them to reach agreement.
- Suggest a timeline for each team member to complete his or her share of the project.
- Share your many good ideas for projects with the team. You are best at thinking of new possible ways to get the work done.

Suggestions for *Friendships*

- Keep the secrets that others may share with you. You like knowing the latest news about friends, and they trust you to keep their news private until they say OK.
- Join multiple activities. You like a wide circle of friends, and you like a variety of activities.
- Have fun joining many activities so long as you don't get too tired from doing too much.
- Tell your friends when you are just talking out loud about possible ideas. Tell them when you decide which idea you want to do.

Suggestions for *Working with Parents and Teachers*

- Ask for grading guidelines so you know exactly what you need to do to get a good grade.
- Ask the teacher for choices if a project seems boring. Many times a teacher will consider an alternative you suggest if it meets the objectives of the lesson.
- Spend some time just playing games or watching movies with your parents. Have fun with them like you have fun with your friends.

ENTJ
Suggestions to help you with your strengths and work with your stretches

Suggestions for *Studying*

- Ask for opportunities for independent study.
- Compete against yourself. Challenge yourself to get one point better on each test.
- Let teachers and parents brag about your accomplishments and praise you for your good grades.
- List the main topics you are studying and challenge yourself to list four to five details under each topic. Arranging details in a logical way under a general title will help you remember them.

Suggestions for *Working with Others*

- Accept that your pace may not be the same as the pace for the team. Check with team members to ask if you are working too fast or too slow for them.
- Compliment team members for what they contribute.
- Ask the team for a timeline of when they will get their share done. Timelines will be important to you.
- Use your good organizational skills to make the ideas of others work with your ideas.

Suggestions for *Friendships*

- Join groups that will let you perform well independently while still being part of the team.
- Ask friends if they want to compete before you start a contest. Not all friends will have as much fun with contests as you.
- Tell friends you are glad to have their friendship. People need to know you like them.

Suggestions for *Working with Parents and Teachers*

- Ask for opportunities to work on projects on your own.
- Tell adults about your ideas. Ask them to tell you about any parts of the idea that might not work. This way they can help you improve your ideas.
- Let your parents and teachers know why you respect them.
- Talk to teachers outside of class so they can get to know you, and you can share your thoughts just with the teacher.

INFP

Suggestions to help you with your strengths and work with your stretches

Suggestions for *Studying*

- Work alone first and then check your work with friends.
- Be careful not to wait too long to start your work. You work well at the last moment but can underestimate how long a job will take you to finish.
- Check to be sure you did not miss any steps or important details. Sometimes you get an idea of what is expected and then don't pay close attention to any changes.
- Finish your work on time. You want it to be perfect and that means sometimes you keep working on it. Make a deadline. Keep to that deadline.

Suggestions for *Working with Others*

- Ask for help from friends when you start to make your ideas happen. You have good ideas but don't always know how to make them work.
- Brainstorm possible ideas with others but make choices on your own.
- Tell others when you are still thinking or deciding. Don't just sit quietly.
- Compliment other team members.
- Ask for feedback if you are unsure of your work.

Suggestions for *Friendships*

- Sort when to support your friends or not. You are a good friend. You stand up for your friends. It is hard for you when your friend does something wrong. Think of a way to help that friend.
- Write your ideas down if you cannot say them. You can decide whether to share the paper with others or not.
- Join a group at school or in the community. It is important for you to be part of a circle of friends.
- Wait if you are upset. All friends argue sometimes. When you are upset wait a while and then try to talk it out with your friends.

Suggestions for *Working with Parents and Teachers*

- Say hello to your teacher each day. Get to know them and let them get to know you.
- Plan something nice to make them smile. They will enjoy your thoughtfulness.
- Admit it when you make a mistake. This will be hard for you. They will still like you and can help you if you need it.
- Ask your parents to tell you stories about their experiences. Sharing stories will help you feel closer.

INTP
Suggestions to help you with your strengths and work with your stretches

Suggestions for *Studying*

- Set a time for independent study.
- Set a goal for what you will accomplish during that time.
- Confirm your recall of the facts by listening to a study group review the information.
- Make word connections between the facts that must be remembered to help you recall them.
- Take breaks between subjects to refresh your mind and get you ready for more study.

Suggestions for *Working with Others*

- Tell the group what you can do well. Offer to help with that part of the task.
- Praise others for their contributions. They will appreciate knowing you respect what they do.
- Let others know when you will complete your part. That can help the group plan so everyone can be done on time.
- Get to know others who do best what you do not do best. You will make a good team when you work together.

Suggestions for *Friendships*

- Enjoy the company of others who like exploring new information as much as you. You may find you have several different groups of friends that you spend time with for different interests.
- Negotiate when you and your friends disagree on the activity to do. Work together to find an agreeable solution.
- Call friends or send them a message. Most times people call you, but they will enjoy calls from you as well.

Suggestions for *Working with Parents and Teachers*

- Volunteer to become the subject expert for a classroom topic. This will let you be your best while helping the class.
- Compliment your teachers or parents for things you respect.
- Let parents know you will listen to their ideas. Then tell them your ideas.
- Ask them to explain their reasons for decisions when the decision is made. That helps you understand better.

ISFP
Suggestions to help you with your strengths and work with your stretches

Suggestions for *Studying*

- Study with a close friend to help you name the most important details to know.
- Study over several days. Cramming is not a style that works for you.
- Laugh and play around and make jokes with the information. It will make the information easier to remember.
- Take frequent breaks in order to keep your energy high.

Suggestions for *Working with Others*

- Smile a lot and let people on the team see all the warm feelings and cooperation you feel on the inside.
- Recognize that you get more energy to work at the last moment. Be sure your teammates are OK with that schedule.
- Let team members know when you feel less comfortable with an assignment. If you feel uncomfortable with an assignment ask if someone can do the task with you.
- Volunteer to help with the specifics. That is a strength for you.

Suggestions for *Friendships*

- Find friendships with outgoing people as well as quiet people. You may enjoy the energy of those who are outgoing and they can enjoy the energy of your quiet and supportive way.
- Enjoy the few close, special friends who help you find adventures in life. Sometimes being with a large group can be overwhelming.
- Do little things to let your friends know you like them. They will appreciate your special ways.

Suggestions for *Working with Parents and Teachers*

- Take some time to get to know your teachers outside of the classroom so they can learn about your hidden potentials. Teachers may underestimate your skills and strengths because you keep them private.
- Tell others when you are still deciding. You like to consider many good ideas and information before you choose. Your being quiet may be confusing to them unless you tell them you are still deciding.
- Pick a place for each of your books and papers so they can be easily found each day. Your parents will appreciate your thoughtfulness in using this way to organize your books.

ISTP
Suggestions to help you with your strengths and work with your stretches

Suggestions for *Studying*

- Ask the teacher for the grading criteria. This lets you know exactly what the teacher will be looking for on a project.
- Ask the teacher to identify the most important points to know for a test; otherwise you may focus on more details than will be necessary.
- Study sections of information over an extended time rather than cramming at the last moment. This may be hard for you, but it will help with your recall.
- Pick a place to put your school books and papers that will be the same each day. This strategy may help you keep better track of papers.

Suggestions for *Working with Others*

- Volunteer to be the researcher of significant facts for the team.
- If other team members want to rush to make a decision, remind them that you are still considering information.
- Monitor your comments to others so they hear your questions and comments but don't feel as if their ideas are not good.
- Use your sense of fun and laughter to keep people working when everyone gets tired.

Suggestions for *Friendships*

- Enjoy the company of a few close friends. You tend to like small groups over large groups.
- Join a social group that gives you a chance to show what you can do well.
- Check to see that your friends are still listening when you tell your stories. Sometimes you can tell too many details and lose their attention.
- Name suggested activities for the group to do. You have lots of possible ideas. One of them will likely work.

Suggestions for *Working with Parents and Teachers*

- Negotiate to change rules you don't understand or like. Ignoring the rules will only lead to trouble.
- To initiate a social conversation, ask your parents (or other adults) about their day.
- Ask the teacher for an outline of the lesson if the class discussion becomes too random or vague for you.
- Share your wealth of information about your favorite topics with your teachers and parents. They will enjoy hearing that part of your experiences.

ISFJ
Suggestions to help you with your strengths and work with your stretches

Suggestions for *Studying*

- Study first on your own. Then study with a friend.
- Study a little each day. Cramming is not your best style.
- Highlight important details. Check with a friend to see if you and your friend agree on what is most important.
- Study one subject at a time.
- Reward yourself with a break with a friend when you finish one subject.

Suggestions for *Working with Others*

- Offer your ideas in the group even if no one asks.
- Use your good team skills for helping friends who start to argue. Keep them focused on what the job is and how to best get the job done.
- Give compliments freely.
- Make a plan for getting the work done. Set due dates. Make sure everyone agrees with them.

Suggestions for *Friendships*

- Help friends know if they are doing something wrong. You are loyal to your friends and may find it hard to believe they would do something wrong. Check with them to learn if it is true. Then be there to help them.
- Trust others who trust you. Build good friendships based on this shared trust.
- Find friends who have the same values as you. Shared values connect you with others.
- Initiate the connection with others. Mostly, others will call you, but you will want to call them as well.

Suggestions for *Working with Parents and Teachers*

- Get to know your teacher on a personal level. Sometimes teachers miss the best part of you because you keep it private.
- Ask for more examples or specifics if you are not clear about the assignment.
- Give compliments to your teachers and parents. They need to know you like what they do.
- Tell your parents when you have plans with friends so they can try not to make family plans that conflict.

ISTJ
Suggestions to help you with your strengths and work with your stretches

Suggestions for *Studying*

- Study on your own first. Then review with friends.
- List the facts. Draw a box under them. Name the main idea that each of the facts supports.
- Study in small units a little each day. Cramming will not be a good way for you to remember.
- Make a study plan. Work on one subject at a time.

Suggestions for *Working with Others*

- Write your thoughts down if you do not get a chance to talk.
- Compliment team members. People don't always know you are glad to be on their team.
- Let others brainstorm. Then tell how you can help them make their ideas happen. That will be the part of the project you like best.
- Volunteer to look for the information the team needs. You can do this easily.

Suggestions for *Friendships*

- Work on your own but have fun with others. You have a love of fun and games when the work is done.
- Enjoy contests where you have a good chance of winning. Make sure your friends also have a chance to win.
- Tell friends you like them if you unintentionally hurt their feelings when you told the truth as you see it. They will want to know you still value their friendship.
- Join groups or teams that do an activity. You have more fun doing something than just talking.

Suggestions for *Working with Parents and Teachers*

- Ask for specific examples if you do not understand the task.
- Ask for the plan. You need to know what is expected. You need to know the schedule for the day so that you can also plan other activities.
- Tell the adults your ideas but realize they have the final say. Explain your ideas so they understand.
- Spend some one-on-one time with the adults talking about a topic that interests you. They will gain respect for your knowledge.

INFJ

Suggestions to help you with your strengths and work with your stretches

Suggestions for *Studying*

- Start assignments as soon as possible. You get upset when you have a lot to do at the last moment.
- Study alone first and then relax with others.
- Schedule regular breaks.
- Use memory tricks for recalling lots of facts.
- Find a quiet place to work.
- Name the main idea. Then list three to four facts under each heading. Use songs, games, or slogans to make the connection between the heading and the facts.

Suggestions for *Working with Others*

- Relax if the group does not work as fast as you like.
- Do your job. Don't worry about others. Let them do their part.
- Give a lot of compliments to others. They may need to know you appreciate them.
- Help friends but be sure you have time to do your work too.

Suggestions for *Friendships*

- Make friends and keep them for a long time. Once a person is your friend they stay your friend.
- Ask your friends if they want your help with their problems. You are always ready to help but sometimes they may want to do it on their own.
- Know that you like the special, close friendship of a few, rather than being popular with everyone.
- Give people what you think they need or like. You have a special talent for knowing what people like and need.
- Reach out to form friendships. Sometimes you wait too long for others to come to you.

Suggestions for *Working with Parents and Teachers*

- Greet your teachers each day.
- Help out with extra projects when you can. Teachers need to get to know you better to see your best side.
- Ask for feedback if you are not sure if the teacher likes you or likes your work.
- Ask your parents to tell you stories about their life and things they know. You are a good listener and learner.

INTJ
Suggestions to help you with your strengths and work with your stretches

Suggestions for *Studying*

- Tell others that you study best when you study on your own.
- Use memory tricks to help you recall details for a test.
- Reread directions. You sometimes skip over parts you don't want to follow.
- Make a schedule for studying. Follow that schedule.

Suggestions for *Working with Others*

- Invite others to share their ideas. Listen for parts that help you get new ideas.
- Tell your ideas for making a project better, rather than telling others why their ideas are wrong.
- Give compliments, when earned, to others on your team.
- Ask a friend to let you know when your ideas are too much for the team. Your excitement about the idea may make you underestimate how much work it will take to make it happen.

Suggestions for *Friendships*

- Join a school or community team that lets your talents shine.
- Participate in sports that have teams but allow for individual skills.
- Avoid frequently telling friends whenever you notice something that they are doing which you think is wrong. Decide if what you have to say will help them do better.
- Ask a friend about their topic of interest. Learn to listen to know what others enjoy.

Suggestions for *Working with Parents and Teachers*

- Avoid debating with your parent or teacher when you think you are right and they are wrong. Listen to their side. Tell your side. Name things you agree on. List things you want to discuss to find the best solution for all.
- Tell your side at most twice. If you do not get your parents or teacher to agree with you, find some part that you can agree on.
- Compliment the adults in your life for things you notice they do well. Compliments matter because they let people know that you care and respect them.

Name _____

Date _____

My Journal Log

Take a moment to write the answers to the following questions. Be prepared to share your thoughts if asked. Circle your preference letter that you are discussing.

(E) **or** (I)

1) *I now know that my strengths include . . .*

_____

_____

2) *I now know that my stretches include . . .*

_____

_____

3) *My natural preference for* _____ *gets me in trouble when I . . .*

_____

_____

4) *My natural preference for* _____ *helps me most when I . . .*

_____

_____

5) *People with my preference are valued and respected because . . .*

_____

_____

6) *People with the opposite preference are valued and respected because . . .*

_____

_____

Name _____

Date _____

My Journal Log

Take a moment to write the answers to the following questions. Be prepared to share your thoughts if asked. Circle your preference letter that you are discussing.

(S) or (N)

1) I now know that my strengths include . . .

_____

_____

2) I now know that my stretches include . . .

_____

_____

3) My natural preference for _____ gets me in trouble when I . . .

_____

_____

4) My natural preference for _____ helps me most when I . . .

_____

_____

5) People with my preference are valued and respected because . . .

_____

_____

6) People with the opposite preference are valued and respected because . . .

_____

_____

Name _____

Date _____

My Journal Log

Take a moment to write the answers to the following questions. Be prepared to share your thoughts if asked. Circle your preference letter that you are discussing.

(T) or (F)

1) *I now know that my strengths include . . .*

_____

_____

2) *I now know that my stretches include . . .*

_____

_____

3) *My natural preference for* _____ *gets me in trouble when I . . .*

_____

_____

4) *My natural preference for* _____ *helps me most when I . . .*

_____

_____

5) *People with my preference are valued and respected because . . .*

_____

_____

6) *People with the opposite preference are valued and respected because . . .*

_____

_____

Name _____

Date _____

My Journal Log

Take a moment to write the answers to the following questions. Be prepared to share your thoughts if asked. Circle your preference letter that you are discussing.

J or **P**

1) *I now know that my strengths include . . .*

_____

_____

2) *I now know that my stretches include . . .*

_____

_____

3) *My natural preference for _____ gets me in trouble when I . . .*

_____

_____

4) *My natural preference for _____ helps me most when I . . .*

_____

_____

5) *People with my preference are valued and respected because . . .*

_____

_____

6) *People with the opposite preference are valued and respected because . . .*

_____

_____

Name _____

Date _____

Summary Journal Log

Now that you have studied about differences and know yourself and your friends better, use this log to tell how you will use that knowledge to help you study, work on teams, and get along with others. Fill in the answers to the questions that follow.

My four-letter type preferences are _____ *(fill in)*

1) *I now know that when I learn and study I do better when I* _____

_____

_____.

2) *I now know that when I work with others I contribute better when I* _____

_____

_____.

3) *I now know that when I have projects to complete I will do better when I* _____

_____

_____.

4) *I now know that when I read facts and details a good way for me to remember them is* _____

_____

_____.

5) *I now know that everyone will not do things the same way. When I do not understand another person's way I will* _____

_____

_____.

Center for Applications of Psychological Type™ (CAPT®)
2815 NW 13th Street, Suite 401
Gainesville, Florida 32609
800.777.2278 *(USA & Canada)*
www.capt.org